TRACTION ENGINES
AND STEAM VEHICLES
IN PICTURES

An 8-nhp three-shaft traction engine No 3789 DCC three-speed with sprung rear axle, made by Charles Burrell Ltd, Thetford, Norfolk, in 1918, and photographed at Raynham Hall, Norfolk, in 1963. It was probably intended for a showmans road locomotive but was sent to the Isle of Man when new in 1921

Traction Engines
And Steam Vehicles
In Pictures

by

ANTHONY BEAUMONT

DAVID & CHARLES : NEWTON ABBOT

7153 4666 0

BY THE SAME AUTHOR
Traction Engine Pictures 1961
Traction Engines on Parade 1962
Rally Traction Engines 1965
Traction Engine Prints 1967
The Organs & Engines of Thursford 1967
Steam Up! Engine and Wagon Pictures 1967
Fair Organs 1968
In preparation – *A Gallery of Old Timers*

Printed in Great Britain
by W. J. Holman Limited Dawlish
For David & Charles (Publishers) Limited
South Devon House Newton Abbot

Contents

Abbreviations and Notes

SC	–	single cylinder
SCC	–	single-crank compound cylinders
DCC	–	double-crank compound cylinders
psi	–	pounds per square inch
TE	–	traction engine
RL	–	road locomotive
SRL	–	showmans road locomotive
PE	–	ploughing engine
RAS	–	Royal Agricultural Society
nhp	–	nominal horsepower. When the steam engine began to be substituted for horses in driving agricultural machinery, the Royal Agricultural Society of England introduced a standard of comparison by estimating the number of horses the engine could replace. This standard, based solely on the piston area, became known as nominal horsepower.
ihp	–	indicated horsepower. This is calculated from the graphical representation of the varying steam pressure in the cylinder, made by an instrument called an indicator.
bhp	–	brake horsepower. Ihp disregards frictional losses in the engine. The actual power available at the flywheel is measured by a brake, generally a friction band round the flywheel rim. This bhp is useful for showing the power available when belt-driving machinery. There was little scientific testing oi TEs' hauling power. The continual variation of loads owing to road conditions would have made such tests of little value.

COPYRIGHTS

Introduction

The steam traction engine in its many diverse forms was pre-eminent both agriculturally and commercially for some ninety years. The pages that follow show a variety of types spanning the years 1880-1947, a period embracing the final designs.

Within the compass of 112 pictures comprising nine main divisions of different classes of vehicles, it is possible either to trace a very sketchy outline of these engines from their earliest days, or to concentrate on the interesting examples which still exist. The second alternative has been chosen for two reasons; firstly because a number of the earlier machines have already been illustrated – sometimes repeatedly – in books or periodicals of quite recent date, and secondly because my photographs made during the past twelve years permit a comprehensive selection. The products of over twenty manufacturers are represented and a large number of photographs are published for the first time. A single illustration is reproduced from an outside source; two are the author's copies.

In my experience, the average reader is rather more interested in 'live engine' pictures than in reproductions of early engravings and old photographs. My *Traction Engine Prints* has already done something to satisfy interest in that direction.

While a number of enthusiasts photographed engines in their former working years with varying degrees of success, I believe that the work of the late Major Ind of East Bergholt, Suffolk, is unique technically and historically. This far-sighted gentleman specialised in ploughing-engine studies, arranging for the machines to be suitably 'posed' under favourable conditions. His photographs, made during the years 1903-31, are in the keeping of the officers of the Road Locomotive Society.

It is out of place here to describe photographic technique in detail, but I suggest that for engine photography a camera giving a larger negative than the popular 35 mm size is preferable. The most up-to-date 'automatic' camera fitted with a wide-aperture lens is certainly unnecessary. All my pictures are taken with a twin-lens reflex camera now fifteen years old, providing a negative $2\frac{1}{4}$ in square. The complete processing work is carried out at home without a dark room.

The heyday of the traction engine dates from the 1890s to the early 1920s. Tracts of land overseas needed large ploughing and threshing machines which only England could supply. The straw- or waste-crop-burning fireboxes of many export or colonial engines were a great asset in regions where coal was scarce. On the home market, the farm traction engine, road locomotive and steam wagon reigned supreme. The early petrol-engined lorries, although much improved by the demands of the 1914-18 war, could not handle very heavy industrial loads. Amusement caterers relied entirely on the showmans locomotive both for haulage and for electricity generating.

The double engine system of cable ploughing with a large range of implements, developed by John Fowler from 1856, was unrivalled. Indeed, as late as 1932 more than twenty pairs of ploughing engines were offered in an East Anglian sale and a few sets remain in work to this day.

The basic traction engine design was settled, generally speaking, in the late 1880s. Cylinders were placed at the leading end of the boiler, the all-gear drive of three or four shafts incorporated a differential, two or three speeds and a rear axle cable winding drum. A front steering straight axle of the simplest mechanical design was invariably coupled to a manstand steering wheel by chains and a high-ratio worm gear drive (plus a certain amount of backlash). Reverse gear was usually, but not always, Stephenson's link motion.

This overall design satisfied the requirements of the agricultural engine well enough until the last made in 1947, a product of William Foster of Lincoln. Showmans locomotives, however, operated at some disadvantage when the same steering arrangement was used in main road traffic of the 1930s. A few amusement caterers continued with their road locomotives after 1945, but the early 1950s saw their total eclipse by diesel, aided by heavy taxation on the steam engine and the rising cost of labour.

In agriculture, the wholesale replacement of the internal-combustion tractor drawing a self-binder by the combine harvester in the mid-1940s made the whole process of separate threshing obsolete. In the transition stage, the tractor with its facility of a power take-off pulley, was much easier to use with a threshing drum than was a traction engine. A six o'clock beginning for an eight o'clock steam start was clearly uneconomical.

County Councils used steam rollers into the 1960s. In many cases the rollers had some advantage of being in steam for several days and were tended with care and affection by drivers of advanced age. In fact it was common for drivers to retire at the same time as their rollers and even purchase them.

Steam wagons were developed to a high degree of efficiency in their final phase up to 1939. Unlike the traction engine of staid traditional design, the wagon used several features found in its petrol-engined rivals. The high-pressure water-tube boilers incorporating superheaters, the totally enclosed undermounted engines enabled the steam wagon to enjoy a brief but marked supremacy. Again, the advent of the lorry diesel engine with its cheap fuel sounded the death-knell of commercial road haulage by steam.

The ubiquitous portable engine is still in demand for some overseas markets in remote regions. Portable steam engines are ideally suited for operation by unskilled labour, and Robey & Co Ltd, Globe Works, Lincoln, are probably the only British firm still making them. Further details of the foregoing groups of engines appear under the separate headings to the picture sections.

Now, thirty years after the demise of steam vehicles, *The Times* of 4 September 1968 reports that serious full-scale commercial experiments in the steam car field are taking place in the USA. The reason for this work is the urgent demand for cars which will not poison the atmosphere with carbon-monoxide exhaust gas.

In the period 1934-50, vast numbers of steam vehicles were sold as scrap metal. Fortunately a few people bought engines for preservation for nostalgic reasons, while some commercial owners retained engines for which they had no further use. Time has proved private purchases of this nature to be remarkably good investments now that engines command such high prices.

The wide public interest in the traction engine as a spectacular 'bygone' dates from 1950, when two friends, driving their engines in a meadow, raced for a barrel of beer. The numerous rallies up and down the country, attended by thousands of people, are now part of the English, and latterly British, scene. It is doubtful whether my photographs could have been so numerous during the working days of traction engines, when such large gatherings of machines never occurred.

Although great efforts of restoration have been carried out on engines which appeared to be a useless mass of metal, the future limiting factor may prove to be the boiler. A steel pressure vessel cannot last indefinitely, and a complete replacement on which the whole motion is erected would certainly be extremely costly. It is to be hoped that such problems lie far ahead.

In conclusion I would emphasise that the illustrations and their supporting text do not aim at anything more than a general pictorial review of engines to-day. Complete technical coverage of the subject may be followed up in the works listed in the bibliography, although some of these may be obtainable only through libraries.

The steam traction engine has an undeniable personality which is not shared by any internal-combustion prime mover. This character emanates, I believe, from the combination of external features – the tall chimney capped with its splendid brass or copper top, the ponderous motion work, and the overall massive sense of power and purpose.

The sonorous exhaust beat of the steam engine at work, sometimes staccato, never harsh but always willing, recalls the name of a Burrell showmans locomotive of 1909 – *A Tryer*.

ANTHONY BEAUMONT

September 1968   South Wootton, King's Lynn

Showmans Road Locomotives

Travelling showmen of the early 1880s began to use electric light, hence self-contained traction-generating engines evolved, replacing horse-drawn transport and portable generating engines.

The first maker of an SRL proper was McLaren in 1880, followed by John Fowler in 1886 and Charles Burrell in 1887. Fowler used DCC engines from the start, although a few early SCs were made. Burrell's first three engines were SCs, but the renowned SCC quickly superseded them and some twenty-four of the latter appeared in the period 1891-6 and infrequently thereafter until 1911. Their first DCC SRL appeared in 1897; after 1911 only DCCs were made until the last in 1930 (built by Richard Garrett at Leiston). The very last SRL was a Foster, built in September 1934.

Apart from these makers, SRLs were produced in much smaller numbers by at least seven other firms. DCC SRLs, without dead-centre positions of the crankshaft when running, were clearly better suited to flywheel belt work than SC engines and particularly SCCs.

Burrell's final designs of SRLs incorporated their standard three-shaft drive with three speeds, usually double-geared on the rear axle which, like the front axle, was on springs. Sizes were rated from 5 to 8 nhp, the largest of 54 normal ihp, but 75 ihp as a continuous maximum. The 8-nhp engines had cylinders $6\frac{3}{4}$ in and $11\frac{1}{4}$ in × 12 in; in a few of the last made, these dimensions were increased to 7 in and $11\frac{1}{2}$ in × 12 in. In full working order these engines weighed $19\frac{3}{4}$ tons, including $1\frac{1}{4}$ tons for the dynamo and exciter.

From 1920 many Burrells were classed as 'Special Scenic'. These were fitted with a boiler mounted exciter driven from the normal front dynamo to excite the field windings of the latter for the heavy starting loads of large scenic railways. A tender-mounted 30-cwt jib crane support was also fitted.

Fowler SRLs were four-shaft designs, the compound cylinders having the valves above and between them with portfaces inclined inwards and downwards. The arrangement was very compact but far less accessible than the outside valve chests of Burrell engines. A few Fowlers had separate exciters located on the boiler water tank top, because the four-shaft design left insufficient room for a boiler-mounted exciter. One Fowler had an exciter mounted on an extra-long smokebox. The final four Fowler SRLs had Burrell-type rear crane fittings and were classed B6 'Super Lion' 10 nhp, with cylinders 7 in and 12 in × 12 in. The continuous ihp was 70-80 with a short period maximum of 115-125. Fowler's last engine, named *Supreme* in 1934, is at present under restoration.

Fosters of Lincoln also made the special scenic type of SRL and their final engines were known as '65 BHP' class with dynamo and exciter. Their 7-nhp 'Class LR' is illustrated.

Showmen achieved surprising haulage feats with long wagon trains of up to ten vehicles totalling 50 tons. Under favourable conditions, speeds of nearly 20 mph were achieved and averages of 10 mph over short journeys were common. After 1926 all RLs were fitted with solid rubber tyres which improved their road performance.

Burrell 'special scenic' SRL No 4000 with DCC cylinders of 8 nhp, three speeds and sprung axles, made 28 February 1925, named *Ex Mayor*. The engine was formerly used by G. T. Tuby & Sons, Doncaster, where this showland owner was once the mayor. 7 ft 'contractors' engine, rear wheels are fitted and the exciter platform is seen behind the chimney. The guides and pulleys for the rear pole crane are prominent. This engine was the fourth-from-last SRL bearing Burrell's name and is seen in a very finely restored condition at least equal to its appearance when new.

A normal Burrell SRL, with front-mounted dynamo only and the full-length canopy of flat design fitted to these earlier engines. *Lady Pride of England* is a 7-nhp DCC machine No 2625 built 10 February 1904 and supplied to W. Buckland, Coventry, and later with Bates' Amusements. Plain steel wheels and ornate painted scrollwork are entirely correct for the period. The dynamo driving belt is coiled on the water tank. A smokebox name ring 'Patent Engine' is correctly applied to the Burrell SCC machines. All SRLs were originally fitted with the 'Road Locomotive' name ring.

Lord Lascelles – a Burrell 'special scenic' three-speed 8-nhp DCC, No 3886, with dynamo and exciter fitted, and probably the sixth SRL made by Burrells, complete with all the 'SS' fittings. It left the works 18 April 1921 for H. Gray, Battersea, and was in showland use until 1939. The electric road lamps were not fitted to the new engine. The dynamo is being driven here and the extension chimney (always used on the fairground) is erected. The governor driving belt is seen above the motion side covers. Plain steel awning supports, unadorned with twisted brass, were not unusual on SRLs.

Burrell *William V* No 3610 is a 'special scenic' 8-nhp engine and the fifth owned by W. Murphy, Newcastle. It is the usual DCC three-shaft, three-speed design, fitted with separate exciter platform and front dynamo, the usual output being 110 V 29.7 kW at 750 rpm. The engine was built 31 August 1914 and was among the first few to be fitted with an exciter platform from the date of making; the 9-in flywheel width was specially made for the large horsepower required on the belt. Here the electrical output is trifling, merely for the canopy lights.

This DCC Burrell No 3933, *Princess Mary*, was supplied to J. Anderton of Exeter on 8 April 1922. It is a 7-nhp three-speed engine, fully spring-mounted and the usual three-shaft design. The brass embellishments are particularly elaborate including a profusion of canopy supports, and stars on the cylinder covers, flywheel, and dynamo pulley centres. The normal continuous bhp was 34 and the working weight approximately 16 tons. As with all dynamos, slide rails are fitted for adjusting the belt tension, and the head of this slide-rail screw is seen beneath the registration number.

Victory is a 'special scenic' Burrell SRL, well-known in England's Eastern Counties from 1920, when new to Charles Thurston of Norwich, until the early war years. In 1947 it was sold by auction for £28. This 8-nhp DCC engine No 3827 was Burrell's first 'SS' SRL to be fitted with exciter and rear crane when new. The working-order weight is 19¾ tons. The three-shaft motion incorporates three speeds and a rear wheel brake is fitted additionally to the brake on the 9-in flywheel rim. The exciter and governor are clearly shown and the maker's mechanical lubricator is fitted near the valve chest cover. The engine has been restored to its original appearance.

A Garrett four-shaft showmans tractor, No 33902, *Medina*, made in 1920 and formerly in showland use with Charles Presland, London E. This is a 4-nhp four-shaft DCC design, sprung on both axles with a normal bhp output of 16 to 18. There is a double drive to the Pickering governor, the belt countershaft for which is seen above the motion cover. Cylinder and valve chest covers are heavily chased in brass. The nearside winding drum cable guides are horizontally mounted on the tender. In common with engines having full-length canopies, the safety valve outlets are encased in brass tubes passing through the roof.

Goliath was originally a War Department DCC Fowler RL No 14424 of 8 nhp with cylinders $6\frac{3}{4}$ in and $11\frac{1}{2}$ in × 12 in, made in 1916. A number of RLs were converted to showland use and this one was rebuilt for P. Collins in 1921 (when the number was changed to 14952) and given the name *Dreadnought*. It was one of the half-dozen or so SRLs of this large size. The dynamo here is below the engine's capacity. The change speed gear pinions are shown and the high-pressure side of the cylinder block. The rear wheels are 7 ft in diameter and the water hose is attached to the steam lifter.

Only two Robey showmans tractors are believed to exist. This is No 41492 new in 1921, a two-speed DCC 4-nhp engine. This view shows the high-pressure side of the cylinder block which is fitted with shrouded safety valves, Pickering governor and valve chest displacement lubricator. A mechanical cylinder lubricator is operated from the low-pressure valve spindle. A rear wheel brake handwheel is seen directly under the steering wheel. The dynamo box-type bracket is a Foster design. The engine was restored single-handed by the owner from a derelict state.

The *Iron Maiden* was named in recent years for a film production of this title in which the engine played a principal part. This Fowler class R3, 7 nhp, was originally *Kitchener*, and new for G. J. Barnes of Portland in 1920, numbered 15657. The sprung front axle design is seen and also the prominent 'dishing' of the disc flywheel – common to DCC Fowler three-speed engines to accommodate the fast-speed gears. These later Fowler SRLs worked at 200 psi. The boiler water-tank here of 132-gallon capacity (rear tank 178 gallons) carries a cast-brass replica of the arms of Leeds.

Another Fowler SRL No 11108 named *Dreadnought* made to the standard four-shaft three-speed design in 1901. The engine was used by the amusement caterer P. Cole in Somerset and is 7 nhp, class R3 'Little Lion' with a maximum flywheel belt horsepower of 40 at 180 psi working pressure. In comparison with the three-shaft Burrells it is apparent that the Fowler cylinders and crankshaft centres are further towards the smoke-box. The rear wheel brake shaft is encased in twisted brass, and plugs for indicating are seen above the low-pressure cylinder drain cocks. The reversing links operating arm projects through the motion cover.

Traction Engines — General Purpose

The term 'traction engine' specifically denotes engines designed for short-distance haulage and flywheel belt driving agricultural machinery. At work, TEs usually towed and drove sets of threshing tackle in the vicinity of the owner's farm or contracting yard, besides engaging in timber and general hauling.

Ransome & May of Ipswich are credited with the first self-moving engine – a portable with added chain drive – in 1842, but in this brief commentary I have omitted historical notes in favour of some aspects concerning TEs commonly seen today.

For home use, TEs were usually fitted with two speeds, rarely three; cylinders were SC, DCC or Burrell's SCC. A single water tank was situated beneath the footplate, and the rear wheels were steel, cross straked, with rim holes for fitting heavy cleats when required. The axles were unsprung.

A speed regulating governor was essential to TEs with the constant and rapid variations of threshing loads which the normal hand regulator could not accommodate. The rear axle winding drum was another important accessory in a working TE. The removal of a large pin or pins from the rear wheel centres permitted the axle and winding drum only to be driven, thus providing a powerful 50-yd cable pull for extricating bogged-down vehicles, the TE remaining stationary.

Final designs of TEs were built by some twenty-five makers, the majority of whom generally used the four-shaft design. The notable exception was Charles Burrell Ltd, who made nearly all their TEs with three shafts, having proved by road tests in 1890 that this layout gave twenty-five per cent more hauling power than four shafts, other variable factors being equal.

When a three-shaft engine travels forwards, the flywheel turns forwards, but in a four-shaft design the flywheel turns backwards when the TE travels forwards. In normal threshing, driving with an open belt, the flywheel must turn backwards. It follows therefore that a three-shaft engine uses the opposite end of its reversing link when threshing, as opposed to travelling forwards. The net result evens out wear on the reversing gear as a whole on a three-shaft engine. Unless threshing is done with a crossed belt, reversing-gear wear on a four-shaft engine tends to be uneven.

TE cylinder sizes were rated from 5 to 8 nhp in SC, SCC and DCC designs with corresponding bhp of about 25 to 38, and hauled loads from about 12 to 25 tons (all as makers' figures). A 5-nhp TE weighs about 9 tons, an 8-nhp about 12 tons.

In DCC engines, a means of starting the motion was necessary when the high-pressure crank stopped on a dead centre. An auxiliary hand-operated valve bypassed a small amount of steam direct to the low-pressure valve-chest merely for starting purposes. In an SC TE, the driver eases the flywheel off a dead centre by hand. Foden DCC engines had a special three-way valve on the cylinder block to permit a correctly proportioned quantity of steam to enter both valve chests simultaneously. This facility gave extra power for fairly brief emergency use.

This single-crank compound TE represents a famous type patented by Frederick Burrell in 1889. The first SCC was made in 1887. The picture shows an 8 nhp, No 2479, made in June 1902, having the early cast-iron chimney and round front axle. The high-pressure cylinder is diagonally above the low-pressure one, their piston rods moving in unison, making their strokes together. Both rods are connected to one crosshead, thence to the single crank. The valve rods also work in unison, being connected to the valve rod proper by the turned linkage shown. Here, the reversing link is down for forward gear.

This SC $8\frac{1}{2}$ in × 12 in 7-nhp Burrell No 3924, new in July 1922, shows the final design; only eleven more Burrell SC TEs were made. The mechanical lubricator linkage to the valve rod is seen, together with a pair of displacement lubricators, one unusually situated on the cylinder cover. This is a two-speed, unsprung TE. The nearside eccentric is here driving the slide valve, the reversing lever being forward and the engine moving forward. The long horizontal rod above the motion operates the regulator. The steering chains have a connecting check chain to prevent over-locking of the front axle.

This 7-nhp SC Allchin TE No 1105 was made at the Globe Works, Northampton, in 1890. The cylinder is $8\frac{1}{2}$ in × 12 in and beneath it the boiler displays the firm's globe-motif transfer. The four-shaft two-speed design is fitted with a rear wheel brake and a cross-arm governor which operates a barrel throttle in the cylinder block. The second shaft bearing-brasses are seen behind the flywheel and it will be noted that the reversing lever is back and the link up for backward motion of the engine, the flywheel turning forwards.

A 5-nhp DCC Burrell No 4045 made in August 1926; a two-speed engine and eleventh from last of the DCC engines made at Thetford. Their completion dates were somewhat haphazard. This gear-side view shows the change-speed pinions, and the gear lever handle projects rearwards. The cylinders are 5 in and 9 in × 10 in stroke, providing 26 bhp for normal continuous work at 200 psi. I believe that the boiler bracket for the front axle is a specially deep design because the first purchaser declined to accept a sprung axle! The steam behind the front wheel comes from the cylinder drain cock pipes.

Aveling & Porter, Rochester, made this 6-nhp four-shaft DCC engine, No 4157, in 1898. The valve chests are above the cylinders and inclined valve spindles are used which can be seen above the circular crosshead guide. The rampant horse emblem appears on the smokebox door which seats on a ring unusually secured by a double row of rivets. The small pulley near the piston rod crosshead takes the governor driving belt. The upper horizontal rod over the motion operates the regulator, the lower rod works the simpling or starting valve. Vertically below the steering wheel the injector water valve rod is seen.

A 7-nhp SC engine made in 1919 by Clayton & Shuttleworth, Lincoln. This is a four-shaft two-speed TE No 48215 with circular trunk crosshead guide and change-speed gears between the hornplates. These later Claytons had the cylinder base machined flat and mounted on a planed saddle attached to the boiler. A similar flat seating is provided for the reversing-shaft bracket and valve guide combined. The ashpan damper is open and its control rod is seen below the steering shaft. The winding-drum is visible behind the rear wheel and just above its rim the usual driver's 'spring' seat.

W. Foster's 7-nhp four-shaft engine No 14593 was new in 1927. The cross-arm governor linkage to the cylinder block $8\frac{1}{2}$ in × 12 in stroke is clearly seen, and the circular cross-head guide will be noted. The motion is at the outward, dead-centre point and the connecting rod horizontal. The eccentric rods are of round section; the link is down for the forward motion of the engine. A Foster mechanical lubricator (commonly used on other makes of engines) is present. The smokebox name ring includes a cast replica of a 1914–18 military tank, signifying the firm's manufacture of these vehicles at Lincoln.

A 5-nhp four-shaft DCC two-speed TE made by McLaren of Leeds in 1918 numbered 1642. A long hollow guide is seen just below the upstanding pressure-gauge. This guide is for the extra third gear change mechanism not fitted here. The two-speed change is on the offside and takes the form of a partially-toothed pinion mating with rack teeth in a circular shaft – similar to the modern bench-drill – being an extremely well-designed arrangement. The injector is mounted high on the tender's side and rear wheel and flywheel brakes are fitted.

Garrett TEs are uncommon today. This example is a four-shaft SC 6-nhp No 34197, made in 1922 with 8 in × 12 in cylinder and working weight of $10\frac{1}{2}$ tons. The maximum bhp was 25. Approximately seventy-eight of this type were made from 1895 to 1931, when a 6 nhp had the distinction of being the last Garrett TE made at Leiston, Suffolk. The rear-wheel 'spuds' hang on a boiler rack, the gears are neatly enclosed and the crosshead is guided by a bored, circular trunk. A hollow-cast brass Gothic G embellishes the smokebox door with the maker's name above.

A Fowler DCC 7-nhp TE of four-shaft design, a type classed as 'Little Lion'. Made in 1921, this engine is numbered 15462 and developed a continuous ihp of 53 to 59. The four splines on which the crankshaft slow-speed gear pinion slides can be seen. Two pairs of straight slide-bars are fitted, also a Pickering governor and a Foster mechanical cylinder lubricator. The boiler inspection manhole is behind the footboard and the water lifter is on the tender's side. The small pipe to the chimney base is the steam blower supply.

This 7-nhp SC four-shaft Fowler is belted to a threshing drum. The cylinder is $8\frac{1}{2}$ in × 12 in, developing a belt horsepower of 36 at the working pressure of 200 psi. The engine carries the number 8886 but the original number was 11594 and 1921 the date of making. The circular hollow pan below the front axle is for the rear wheel cleats. The slide bars are a straight angled design. A typical Fowler pump water pipe passes over the third shaft gear case to the boiler check valve. Note the double lever linkage to the cylinder drain cocks.

C

A Ruston & Proctor SC engine of 8-nhp four-shaft design, numbered 49804 and made in 1910 at the Sheaf Works, Lincoln. The Proctor name dates from 1840, R & P 1857-1918. The steering control is on the nearside but different makers and different engine types varied this position. A strongly-designed motion plate braces the upper hornplates; a standard Pickering governor is fitted and the gear pinions are neatly cased. Twisted links of the steering chains are a Ruston feature. The cylinder is bolted to a flat boiler seating.

The small firm of Fowell & Co Ltd, St Ives, Hunts, made 101 TEs 1877-1922. This engine, No 103, is one of the seven made with an extra-slow third speed (based on F. Savage's patent). It is one of the two surviving 8-nhp engines of the sixty-five made. The three-shaft design was used and it is noticeable that the whole motion layout is set well back on the boiler. The trunk guide is circular, and a standard cross-arm governor turns a barrel throttle between the upper regulator chest and the valve chest. The front axle is set under the boiler to facilitate turning. The valve chest cover bears the firm's finely-cast nameplate dated 1913.

SC Marshall 7-nhp four-shaft two-speed engine, number 61880, built for the Royal Agricultural Show 1913. The Britannia Works, Gainsborough, Lincs, was in the first rank of TE makers. The engines are easily identified by the stout wheel construction, with heavy spokes which, on the front wheels, alternate on each side of the rim T-piece. The cross-arm governor, bored crosshead guide and rectangular front 'spud' pan are other features of late Marshall TEs. Indicating plugs are seen on the cylinder and there is a blower pipe to the chimney base. Parts of a steam wagon appear between chimney and cylinder.

Ruston & Hornsby succeeded Ruston & Proctor in 1919. This R & H DCC is thought to be unique as the only compound left of the make. It is 7-nhp, four-shaft, numbered 122300 and made in 1924. The full-length canopy is unusual for a TE, although RLs were fitted with three-quarter canopies to exclude the chimney. This low-pressure cylinder view shows that the valve rod guide is supported from the valve chest. The cylinders are secured on a flat seating and, like the Ruston & Proctor TE illustrated, the steering-chain links are set over or twisted.

This four-shaft 6-nhp two-speed TE made by Robey, Globe Works, Lincoln, is one of only three Robeys seen by the author. The steering is on the nearside, the driver is opening the regulator and the ashpan damper is fully open. The reverse gear eccentric rod shows unsharp because of its relatively fast movement. The large manhole is secured inside the boiler shell by a pair of heavy bridge clamps and bolts. Robey's large star and gold medal transfer decorates the boiler cladding. The engine number is 42675 and the date of making 1927.

This 4-nhp tractor of DCC design with two speeds was made by Aveling & Porter, Rochester, in 1918, and numbered 9267. It is sprung on both axles and was converted to a roller from 1953 to 1965. This accounts for the rear rolls seen, now fitted with pressed-on rubber tyres, and also the non-standard front wheels, similarly tyred. Cylinders are $4\frac{5}{8}$ in and 7 in × 8 in, developing about 21 bhp at 180 psi maximum. The outside slide valves will be noted and the simpling steam pipe connecting the high- and low-pressure valve chests. The steering gears are covered – a most desirable feature.

The 'Wellington' 4-nhp three-shaft tractor was made by William Foster, Lincoln, who introduced this design in 1903. This example is sprung on both axles, the rear axle being supported on elliptical springs outside the hornplates patented by the firm in 1909 and 1911. The cylinder block with a flat base contains compound cylinders $4\frac{1}{2}$ in and $6\frac{3}{4}$ in × 9 in, providing a continuous bhp of 18 at 210 psi. This example is No 13031, made in 1913. The working-order weight is 6 tons. Two speeds are provided. The 183-gallon side water tanks are probably replacements of welded construction. The driver is handling both regular and reversing lever.

A Burrell DCC tractor of 4-nhp three-speed three-shaft design on springs, made in 1912, number 3397. Very few Burrell tractors exist. The working pressure was 200 psi with $4\frac{1}{2}$ in and $7\frac{1}{2}$ in × $8\frac{1}{2}$ in cylinders. The design dates from 1906 when rubber tyres were specified. The overlap of the front cylinder covers will be noted on the typical Burrell compound block. The low-speed gear is the outermost crankshaft pinion seen with the intermediate and high gear pinions near the hornplate. The 'empty' weight was but 56 lb under 5 tons.

This compact tractor was made by Mann's Patent Steam Cart & Wagon Co, Hunslet, Leeds. It was their final design using the four-shaft DCC layout of their wagon. The three speeds and rear axle differential are entirely between the hornplates. The over-mounted rear water tank holds 200 gallons and the driver's position is a somewhat precarious perch on the offside where the side firebox door was located. The cylinders are 4 in and $6\frac{3}{8}$ in × 7 in developing 30 ihp at 200 psi. The feed-pump is seen driven at reduced crankshaft speed by the countershaft disc crank. The tractor is No 1425 made in 1920.

This Fowler 'Tiger' 3-nhp four-shaft tractor is shown travelling at some 12 mph. It was made in 1920 and numbered 15629. The DCC cylinders are the standard Fowler design with inclined valve spindles. The $4\frac{1}{2}$ in and $7\frac{1}{2}$ in × 9 in cylinders developed a continuous ihp of 29 to 33, which figures underrate the arbitrary nhp figure. The wood-block rear wheels are conspicuous and rarely seen now. Other details shown include rear wheel and flywheel brakes, Pickering governor, mechanical lubricator and the reversing lever with its notched quadrant for 'linking up' in forward or reverse gear. The weight is $6\frac{1}{4}$ tons and hauling power about 10 tons.

No 1837 DCC tractor was made by J. & H. McLaren in 1936 and is their final design, towards the end of the steam era. The rating is 4 nhp and two speeds are fitted. Part of the neat change speed mechanism mentioned on an earlier page can be seen. Cylinders of $4\frac{1}{2}$ in and $7\frac{1}{2}$ in × $8\frac{1}{2}$ in provide a maximum ihp of 40 at 200 psi. A Ramsbottom-type safety valve of hollow cast U design is carried on the regulator chest cover; the steering worm is below the worm wheel to clear the water tank, and the delivery pipe from the feed pump enters the boiler via the side check valve.

Known as the 'oilbath' tractor, this 4-nhp example, No 7871, was made by Wallis & Steevens, Basingstoke, in 1926. The piston and valve rods of the $4\frac{3}{4}$ in and $8\frac{1}{4}$ in × 9 in cylinders pass into an oilbath via packed glands, the one for the high-pressure valve rod showing in the cut out side plate. The working weight is $5\frac{1}{2}$ tons and the 170-psi working pressure provided a 25 maximum bhp. These tractors were made 1905-30. This one shows an extensively repaired rear wheel and a pristine gold medal transfer – now unobtainable from the makers.

A Ransomes Sims & Jefferies tractor with DCC cylinders $4\frac{1}{2}$ in and $7\frac{1}{2}$ in × 8 in, No 39088, made at Ipswich in 1928. At the working pressure of 180 psi up to 20 flywheel bhp was claimed. The standard flywheel was 3-ft diameter, and the one shown would be too small for threshing work unless the engine ran at an excessive speed. The near-vertical hornplate mounted feed-pump is seen above the water tank through which the steering-wheel shaft passes in a tunnel. The regulator steam chest carries a Gardiner governor and the starting valve is operated by the upper horizontal rod.

Road Locomotives and Special Types

Charles Burrell made the world's first heavy haulage road engine in 1856. A fine commemorative plaque of this engine with its Boydell 'Patent Railway' wheels has adorned the old drawing office wall of the derelict Thetford works since 1958.

From this beginning, the long line of road engines stretches to the early 1930s and prodigious feats of steam road-haulage continued for a further ten years.

The first RLs were SC machines but a few were fitted with duplex cylinders. These early engines differed little from the normal TEs of the day except for a second water tank and motion side covers. In the early years of experiment, many designs of RLs and special types were tried which may be followed up by referring to the bibliography.

In 1881 Fowlers patented the compound cylinder block which soon became standard for RLs, followed by Burrell's SCC in 1891. Sprung axles were common from the late 1880s and by the 1890s RLs had reached their final general design incorporating three speeds. Rubber-tyred wheels were obligatory from 1926.

While nearly all makers produced RLs, the engines of Fowler, Burrell and McLaren were most widely used. From 1886 three 12-nhp McLaren RLs performed admirably for the French parcels service, maintaining an 8-mph average on the 70-mile journey from Lyons to Grenoble, and covering some 15,000 miles per year over very poor roads.

Burrell's largest RL, classed 'Contractors', is a typical example of the final phase with cylinders of 7 in and $11\frac{1}{2}$ in × 12 in. (See also final SRLs, page 10.) They worked at 200 psi with 7-ft rear wheels and 4 ft $7\frac{1}{2}$ front. The maker's figure of hauling power was 45 tons on a 1-in-18 gradient, but as with the majority of engines this figure could be exceeded considerably. In working order these RLs weighed $15\frac{3}{4}$ tons.

The Fowler 'Big Lion' and 'Super Lion' class B6 RLs were also used by large contractors, until the 1940s, for loads too bulky for the railways. In 1938 the world's largest load, a steam accumulator weighing 90 tons and measuring 70 ft by 12 ft diameter, was hauled from Annan, Scotland, to London's Beckton gasworks – 325 miles in eighteen travelling days. Three 10-nhp Fowlers were used, two for towing, one in reserve. Less bulky but ever heavier loads were handled in the 1930s.

The crane TE was made by several firms. Aveling & Porter's crane engine did well in the RAS trials of 1870, while the Bray engine of 1862 which worked in Woolwich Dockyard was the first engine of the type. In engineering works, crane engines were very convenient for fetching 4 to 5-ton loads from a railway yard and depositing them in the precise location required.

The special Fowler winding and hauling engine illustrated may appear to be a ploughing engine, but in fact it was a frustrated Russian military export order of 1917. Students will notice that the winding gearing has something in common with Fowler's slanting shaft road wheel transmission of the early 1860s.

Several makers produced crane engines. Burrells made thirty-two from 1886 and *The Lark* illustrated here was the last in 1927 and the last-but-one DCC made at Thetford. The usual three-shaft design is 8 nhp, three speeds, No 4074. Apart from the extra-strong forecarriage and wheels, the engine itself has all the extra equipment found in an RL. The decorative brass on the motion covers indicates that they were handy spares in Burrell's last months. The front cable winch is bevel gear driven from the crankshaft, the final winch drive being worm and worm wheel. The nominal crane lift was 4 tons.

D

Emperor is a SCC 10-nhp Burrell crane engine, made as a SRL in 1895, No 1876. The cylinders are probably 7 in and $11\frac{1}{2}$ in × 12 in. Burrells used it for many years at their Thetford Works. Now seventy-four years old, the engine is seen finely restored in 1963 with safety valves, lifting and complete crane equipment. The shaft drive to the chain winch drum is detailed, the cross-arm governor is behind the nearer jib stay and the bracket for the former boiler water tank remains in position. Canopy supports are authentic early Burrell design, but the outsize whistle is a much later addition.

This 5-nhp DCC Burrell RL No 4066 is almost certainly the sixth-from-last DCC made at Thetford. This engine is dated 26 April 1927. The cylinders are $5\frac{1}{2}$ in and 9 in × 10 in, developing a normal bhp of 26 at 200 psi. The specified hauling power was 25 tons on a 1-in-18 slope. The reversing lever is in mid-gear showing the link motion in mid-position. The cylinder communicating pipe (simpling valve attached) is seen and the injector is prominent behind the rear wheel. The flywheel brake handwheel shows below the steering wheel. Rubber tyres would have been fitted to the rear wheels when new.

No 3657, a 6-nhp Burrell RL on springs, built in 1915, may have been made as a TE although the boiler water tank and steering gear arrangement are standard RL design. The SCC cylinder block (6 in and 10 in × 10 in), bar crosshead guides and the single drive to both valve spindles can be seen, together with a flywheel brake. The slight backward inclination of the cylinders enables the crankshaft to be set lower to compensate for the diagonal cylinders. The driver is handling the regulator.

Made in 1920, this Burrell DCC RL is 5-nhp No 3856, with three speeds and sprung axles. The cylinders are $5\frac{1}{2}$ in and 9 in × 10 in which develop a normal ihp of 30. The maker's unladen weight was given as $10\frac{1}{2}$ tons with 1 ton added for working order. Total water-tank capacity is 235 gallons. The three-quarter-length canopy was usual for RLs; the disc flywheel and covered motion minimised the distraction to horse traffic. The cylinder block here is complete with Pickering governor, mechanical lubricator and a normal size whistle. 8 to 12 miles could be covered without water replenishment with an average 25-ton load.

A large number of these Fowler gun-hauling and winding engines were intended for Russia during the First World War. Events caused the engines to be sold here from 1917 for general work. Classed as 'Little Lion', the cylinders are $6\frac{3}{8}$ in and 11 in × 12 in developing a short maximum ihp of 87 to 95 at 200 psi. The winch is driven by the double bevel-geared inclined shaft and the crankshaft bevel can be disengaged on its four splines. A dog clutch operated by the horizontal lever puts the winch in work. The engine's number is 14933 and maker's date 1917.

R. Garrett, Leiston, Suffolk, made a bold attempt to counter the increasing competition from internal-combustion farm tractors by producing this 5-ton 'Agrimotor' or 'Suffolk Punch' in 1917-18. Only eight were made; this is No 33180. The first 'Fordson' paraffin tractors of 1917 weighed but 23 cwt. The 'Agrimotor' DCC piston-valved cylinders on a short locomotive boiler developed 40 bhp using superheated steam at 200 psi. The forward position of the driver, the Ackerman steering, and the final roller chain drive inside the nearside rear wheel will be noted. The upper of the two control levers is the regulator, the lower lever is the two-speed change.

Another Fowler DCC four-shaft engine but of 6 nhp, this being No 15466 made in 1921 and new to the Duke of Northumberland. Although fitted with the extra boiler water tank, this engine may be classed as a tractor or RL. The cylinders are 6 in and $10\frac{1}{2}$ in × 12 in providing 48 to 53 continuous ihp at 200 psi. Straight angled guide-bars are seen here, the Fowler direct-acting governor, rear wheel brake and a belt guide roller on the tank top. The chimney hinges forwards. Nominal hauling power was 20 tons, and the working weight $11\frac{1}{2}$ tons.

No 9904 is an RL of 7 nhp made by John Fowler Ltd, Leeds, in 1904, with DCC cylinders $6\frac{3}{8}$ in and 11 in × 12 in indicating 53 to 59 horsepower at 180 psi for continuous work. In later years, Fowler named RLs under the general term 'tractor'. The average load hauled was at least 25 tons, and in general the motion work is like the Fowler 7 nhp shown in the TE section. Maximum water tank capacity is 300 gallons and the large equalising pipe is seen below the boiler tank. The smokebox has been repaired by an additional plate on the lower half.

A light RL made by Aveling & Porter, Rochester, in 1928 and numbered 12186, weighing about 8 tons. The DCC cylinders are rated 6 nhp and two speeds are fitted. Outside slide valves are fitted here although some engines of this type had outside piston valves. The steering shaft passes through the unusually deep water tank to which the neatly encased worm steering gear is attached. The wheels are of all-cast design in one unit. The winding drum shows behind the rear wheel, and the rear wheel screw-applied brake handwheel on the offside shows above the tender's coal rails.

This Fowler four-shaft two-speed TE number 15771 was built in 1926. It is of 8 nhp, weighing 12 tons, and a 'special' by virtue of the extra-wide wheels for fenland use. The motion controls seen behind the flywheel are the regulator (upper rod), the simpling starting control button, and – further to the rear – the cylinder drain valves lever. Beneath this is the change-speed lever and the vertical reverse lever. The flywheel is not 'dished' as there is no third speed. The cylinder block is adorned with an outsize whistle and carries a Pickering governor. Four straight guide-bars carry the two crossheads.

G. Elston, Welby, Lincs, made six small portables and this 10 ft 8 in long, single-speed TE dated 1899-1900, No 7. It is rated 2 nhp with a SC $5\frac{5}{8}$ in × $6\frac{1}{2}$ in taking steam at 150 psi from a boiler made by Grantham Boiler & Crank Co Ltd. Two Salter safety valves are seen on the regulator chest. The mechanical lubricator is a later addition. Both front and rear wheels have single T-rings. A partly-seen spectator shows the general scale of this uniquely small commercial TE. Other interesting details are the Porter governor and marine-type crank-head bearing. The crankshaft pinion is not in place.

This 8-nhp McLaren, Leeds, DCC RL No 1421 was made in 1913 and worked on the making of Cranwell Aerodrome. It is a four-shaft three-speed design said to weigh $11\frac{3}{4}$ tons; I assess its weight as at least 1 ton heavier. The outside slide valve cylinder-block has bores of $6\frac{1}{4}$ in and $10\frac{3}{4}$ in × 12 in stroke, taking steam at 200 psi. The rubber blocks on the rear wheels are unusual and the neat spherical turning on the link lifting arm and the general light design of the reversing gear will be noted. The front axle spring passes through the perch bracket.

Ploughing Engines

The earliest record of an attempt to harness steam power to land cultivation appears to be David Ramsey's patent of 1630, which probably envisaged some form of direct-traction plough. The first known method of cable ploughing was Major Pratt's 1811 patent which covered a portable engine, placed centrally in a field, pulling a plough with an endless cable via angled pulley anchors. The Burrell Boydell engine of 1856 was the first to pull a plough directly as a working proposition.

By 1854 John Fowler had designed the forerunner of the world's largest range of PEs which were to be exported universally over a period of sixty-five years. His earliest PEs and balance ploughs were made by Ransomes & Sims and Clayton & Shuttleworth. A variety of other makes of engines also cultivated by forking or digging, with apparatus forming integral attachments. Several engine firms built PEs with cable drums mounted horizontally or vertically on the boiler or, in two cases, within the rear wheel rims.

The Fowler PEs of 1862 were moved over the ground by means of a long, slanting shaft from the crankshaft to the rear axle with bevel gearing transmission. The horizontal cable drum was under the boiler, driven by a vertical shaft and reduction spur gearing as in later engines. In 1859 Fowler patented a self-gripping pulley or 'clip-drum' which provided an automatic friction-grip on half a turn of the cable. Duplex-cylinder PEs were in use by 1870 and by 1882 DCC PEs appeared, incorporating a two-speed ploughing gear like that shown on the McLaren PE illustrated. In 1895 four Fowler DCC types were in production and of similar design to those appearing in the pictures.

The largest DCC of this period, made for export, had cylinders 8 in and 14 in × 14 in and was rated at 20 nhp. These engines weighed about 21 tons with rear wheels 7 ft × 26 in, front 5 ft 6 in × 20 in. The overall length was 24 ft 11 in, width 9 ft 6½ in. The most powerful PEs used here were a special pair in Lincolnshire with cylinders 9 in and 15 in × 15 in. They went to Malaya in 1950. One very large PE rated at 30 nhp was exported to Italy in 1928.

The BB and BB1 classes which are seen today were widely used in the UK after their introduction in 1913 and 1918 respectively. A few pairs are still at work – forty or more years after they left Fowler's Steam Plough Works, Leeds. Cylinder sizes of the BB were 6¾ in and 11½ in × 12 in, usually with two-speed ploughing gear (14 nhp) or 7 in and 12 in × 12 in, usually with single-speed ploughing gear (16 nhp). BB1 engines had the latter cylinder sizes, slightly larger grate areas, and were also rated at 16 nhp.

During 1914-18 a number of class AA7 engines were diverted from export orders to the UK and one is shown here. The cylinders were 7½ in and 13 in × 12 in with a rated nhp of 18. They were used mainly for ploughing, whereas the BB class usually operated with cultivators at a slightly higher cable speed.

Approximately twenty-eight of this Fowler BB1 type of 16-nhp ploughing engine exist and are generally described above. The inclined valve rods to the DCC cylinders are clearly seen here and the single locomotive-type bar crosshead-guide which the slide embraces. The large bevel gear at the upper end of the vertical cable drum shaft revolves with the crankshaft, the heavy dog clutch beneath the flywheel engages the small, guarded pinion meshing with the cable drum gear. The long low-pressure piston tail-rod guide distinguishes these BB1s from BB PEs. This engine is No 15219 made in 1918. For ploughing it would develop about 200 ihp for brief bursts.

Fowler PE No 15340, class BB1, 16 nhp, made in 1919, is shown here with the owner (right) and drivers during tree-pulling work in 1960. A few turns of the flywheel and the plough cable uproots large trees. This is the LH engine of the pair. Two-speed ploughing gear is fitted and the low-pressure guide-bar, crosshead and connecting rod are well shown. A boss showing below the crosshead is the collar on the reversing shaft. A small lever below the flywheel allows a pawl to drop into ratchet teeth on the cable drum when paying out the cable. Rear wheel cleats are in position.

Fowler BB1 No 15172, 16 nhp, 1918, is here seen with its new owner a quarter-mile from the author's home, after several years of stationary steam-sterilising. The front wheel bearing bushes are badly worn and there is a makeshift chimney held to a very thin smokebox with temporary cleats. The engine has single-speed ploughing gear. The heavy shackle and screw adjusting link for the steering rods show well. There is 180 psi of steam and the safety valve is lifting slightly. The cover of the worm steering gear has been removed in order to straighten the shaft for the 12-mile journey.

No 15340 from the offside, photographed when cultivating. The engine is paying out the 600-yd cable, perfectly wound on the drum; the fire has been made up for the next pull. The high-pressure crank-head bearing shows the tapered cotter fitting secured by a long stud and adjusting nut. All four cylinder drain valves are worked from the single lever and a rod system. A diamond braced lever and collar operates the change-speed pinion. Cylinder oiling is effected by mechanical and displacement lubricators. The injector water feed pipe enters the boiler near the drum gearwheel, and a blower pipe with control valve passes into the chimney base.

A McLaren PE No 1541 DCC, 12 nhp, made in 1918 with two-speed ploughing gear arranged on a pair of vertical shafts designed like the back gearing of a centre lathe. The outside valve chests will be noted; the high-pressure chest contains a balanced slide valve; there are straight guide-bars and long crosshead. Like the McLaren RL illustrated on a previous page, the link motion is finely turned and the valve rod guide is set well back from the chest. The steering wheel is on the offside. Only three McLaren PEs are believed to exist.

This Fowler class AA7 PE represents the largest size (21 tons) normally used in the UK. No 15236 was made in 1917 and is named *Bessie*, with DCC cylinders, 7 in and 12 in × 12 in, 18 nhp, with single-speed ploughing gear. While the cylinders are the same bore and stroke as the BB class, the AA boiler is 2 ft 9¾ in diameter compared with 2 ft 6¾ in of the BB. The cable speed is slightly lower with a greater pull, designed specially for ploughing. Double crosshead guide-bars are seen, the driver handles the regulator, and the small handwheel near the flywheel rim operates a friction brake on the vertical ploughing shaft.

Rollers

The earliest form of steam roller was a Bray traction engine which towed a separate heavy roller near Hyde Park in 1859. In the following year a complete steam roller of French design worked in the Bois de Boulogne. By 1865 eight rollers weighing 15 tons, of another French design, were working in Paris; some of these were made by Manning Wardle & Co of Leeds. Another early three-roll machine was designed jointly by W. Clark in India and F. W. Batho in Birmingham, and was made by Worsdell & Evans, Birmingham, in 1862. It worked in India for several years.

To the general public, the steam roller of later years recalls the brass rampant horse and 'Invicta' (unconquered) scroll, these being the trademark of Thomas Aveling of Rochester from 1865, later of Aveling & Porter, then Aveling Barford of Grantham from 1934. This emblem was proudly carried by approximately 8,000 steam rollers both in Britain and in seventy overseas countries up to 1947.

Aveling's first roller in 1865 was, like the earliest effort, a combination of a TE and a separate plain roll. In this case Aveling's TE pulled a cast-iron section of bridge pier, 10 ft diameter and 9 ft wide, weighing 15 tons. His next roller in 1866 was a self-contained machine of TE design with side rear wheels and was used near Hyde Park. In 1867 a similar roller went to Liverpool Corporation.

By 1878 Aveling's rollers resembled the now familiar designs and in that year one was sold to the municipality of Oslo. This 10-ton roller worked there until 1960 when it was retired to the Oslo Technical Museum with honour and festivity as the oldest steam roller in existence. The oldest roller in the UK is an 1882 machine kept by Aveling Barford Ltd at Grantham, and the second oldest is illustrated here. All these are SC four-shaft designs.

Many rollers were without a differential gear, but cornering was aided by the removal of hub locking pins, permitting one wheel to rotate freely on its axle. Cylinder designs were SC, SCC, DCC and duplex; piston or slide valves were used. Six to 16-ton rollers were generally available from a number of makers, and a few 18 and 20-ton rollers were made. Two speeds were standard.

In the mid-1920s the asphalt road surfaces required a roller with a quick reverse gear to avoid any pause on the soft material. Wallis & Steevens produced their 'Advance' series to meet this demand; an example is illustrated.

Road-scarifying attachments were usually fitted to rollers. Heavy tines were screw-operated for depth and a narrow trench was hand-picked through the road surface for a start.

I recall a beautifully kept Aveling & Porter convertible roller working on the Sandringham Estate in the 1920s, bearing the owner's plate 'H.M. The King' in addition to the name *Persimmon* – the royal Derby winner. It passed to a dealer who scrapped it.

An Aveling & Porter DCC piston valve roller, No 14121, made in 1931, rated 7 nhp, 12 tons, type W. Piston valves were superseded by outside slide valves in the last designs because of a tendency to water trapping and damage, especially when descending hills with an overfull boiler. Spring relief drain valves are seen here. The two-speed gear-pinion slides on the squared crankshaft end. A worm wheel and rack-controlled Price scarifier is attached, the rear axle taking the pull by the stout tie-rod. An extra-low geared steering worm wheel is seen and above it the typical A & P diagonal boiler feed pump.

This Aveling & Porter SC roller, four-shaft, 10-ton, 7-nhp, No 2018, is probably the sixth-from-oldest A & P roller in existence in the world. It was made in 1884 and as seen is in full working order. In general the design changed little during the next fifty years. The diagonal boiler pump was introduced in 1879. This roller was probably made to work at 140 psi when new with nominal speed of 1 mph and 2¾ mph in the two gears. There is a displacement lubricator on the valve chest, the regulator lever protrudes above the driver's head; twin adjustable safety valves and front fork eyes for the roll scrapers are some other items of interest.

Formerly in use by Ipswich Corporation, this 8-ton SC roller, three-shaft design, No 34084, was made by Garretts, Leiston, in 1921. It is of specially light design, using cast steel for the channel-section front roll fork and roll head. Rated 5 nhp at 160 psi, it may be the last-remaining Garrett made as a roller. The two-speed gear pinions are covered and there are adjustable rear roll scrapers. Steering chain drums are on extensions outside the hornplates, and an auxiliary valve and steam pipe is fitted to the cylinder block – probably for tar-heating. The maker's brass G appears on the head casting.

An Aveling-Barford SC piston-valve 10-ton roller No AC 605, built at Grantham in 1937 and having features of the last Ruston rollers which Aveling-Barford took over. Apart from water-ballast rolls, this machine shows the ultimate steam roller design with neat cylinder block surmounted by shrouded safety valves with a canopy vent pipe. The front roll spokes are cast T-section and the rear are of similar clean design. The flywheel is of small diameter and the rear water tanks are divided each side of the footplate. The smokebox is attached to the boiler by an angled flanged and bolted joint.

Another but smaller roller by Fowlers, No 15973, 1924, with four-shaft DCC design, weighing approximately 6 tons. The cylinders, 5¼ in and 9 in × 9 in of standard Fowler design, carry a mechanical lubricator of generous size, single safety valve normally lifting at 200 psi, and an organ pipe whistle. The front roll head casting is supported by a steel plate extension of the smokebox. A boiler manhole is shown below the motion cover. The reversing lever is being moved forward for forward gear while the regulator has been closed. Note the set of firing implements hanging on the rear canopy support.

No 18651 is an 8-ton four-shaft roller made by Fowlers in 1930. The SC is 5 nhp, probably 8 in × 10 in; working pressure 140 psi. There is a neatly cased steering worm-gear on the offside and the spirally cast grooves in the chain drum are prominent. Bolt fixing of the roll spokes can be seen, and here the renewable rolls are very well worn on the rear. In common with other rollers there is no governor because rollers are not designed for belt driving. Spring-loaded scrapers are fitted and the canvas canopy screens added some comfort in working days.

This 'Advance' roller made by Wallis & Steevens, Basingstoke, in 1925 is No 7836, with twin or duplex cylinders, each 5 in × 10 in, operated by inside piston valves. There are therefore two pairs of circular covers in line on the cylinder block. The working weight is approximately $9\frac{1}{4}$ tons and the side water tanks provide evenly distributed fore-and-aft weight. There is no flywheel (unnecessary with duplex cylinders with cranks at 90°). A quick reverse facilitates the rolling of elastic materials. The rear axle is in halves, permitting adjustable rear rolls for road camber and the steering is a positive bevel worm and rack gear.

A Wallis & Steevens 10-ton roller made at Basingstoke, Hants, c 1905, fitted with the patent 'Expansion' valve gear and two speeds. Photographed when new at the works and copied by the author. The considerable thickness of the rolls when new should be noted and the rearward position of the reversing shaft to allow for the extra set of links near the cross-arm governor. The front roll fork casting pivots laterally on the large pin seen which passes through the yoke embracing the fork head steering pivot. The single cylinder, $7\frac{1}{2}$ in × 10 in, carries a lubricator on the front cover and takes steam at 120 psi.

A Wallis & Steevens 'Simplicity'-type roller of almost 3 tons working weight, No 7939, made in 1927. Introduced in 1925 for export to China, the inclined boiler contains a replaceable, circular, stayless firebox. The single cylinder is 4 in × 6 in, driving the rear rolls, 3 ft 9 in diameter, via a three-shaft gearing and one speed. The wedge-shaped water tank holds 75 gallons. An injector is seen on the nearside and also the direct worm drive to the front steering roll. The cylinder has twin safety valves, mechanical lubricator and an upstanding pressure-gauge. Unlike orthodox roller smokeboxes, this one is easily accessible for tube cleaning.

A 10-ton Burrell roller of three-shaft DCC design, having cylinders 5 in and 9 in × 9 in taking steam at 160 psi. This engine is No 3993, rated 6 nhp, was made 8 October 1924, and is fitted with Hosack's scarifier on the offside. The plain stovepipe chimney fitted is authentic Burrell although not so common on later engines as the brass or copper bell-topped design. A winding drum and guide rollers are fitted and the motion side cover is cut away for the boiler feed pump valve. A pair of small water level test cocks are visible on the tender's tank. The rolls are almost unworn.

A DCC Burrell 8-ton roller with cylinders 5 in and 8½ in × 9 in working at 160 psi. This example, No 4067, was made 23 April 1927, being the sixth-from-last Thetford-built roller and named *Hero*. It is fitted with a double tined Price's scarifier, two speeds, mechanical and displacement cylinder lubricators and rear roll scrapers. The elegant chimney, shapely roll front and general proportions combine, in my opinion, to form the finest looking roller of all. The fork pivot can move sideways at the top of its housing and the ornamental, cursively written 'Burrell' appears on the roll head. For the portrait we may wish the gallon oil-can elsewhere!

Many firms made rollers convertible to traction engines by replacing the flange bolted front casting by another carrying normal TE wheels. This Marshall roller No 88314 SC made in 1937 is this convertible type and of 8 tons, rated 4-nhp, with cylinder $6\frac{1}{2}$ in × 9 in working at 180 psi. The cylinder is mounted on a flat boiler seating and a circular trunk-guide is fitted. The forward position of the reversing lever denotes forward motion of the roller and the rear brake screw handle shows over the tender. Securing darts of the inclined smokebox door show the awkwardness of tube cleaning on normally-designed rollers.

An unusual two-roll tandem design by Robey of Globe Works, Lincoln. The weight is 7 tons and the building date 1924, No 42071. It is one of some four examples remaining and was rebuilt in 1933 when the DCC cylinder covering may have been added. The twin steel channel frame supports a locomotive-type boiler of stayless round firebox design supplying the 4 in and $7\frac{1}{4}$ in × 7 in cylinders at 200 psi. The steering is a positive worm and quadrant, and the front roll is in three sections. The small flywheel permits a quick reverse via the normal Stephenson's link motion. Maximum bhp was 25 and speed 4 mph.

A larger Marshall roller of 10 tons, SC design No 76797, made in 1923, classed 'Q' and named *Mary*. The distinctive Marshall front casting resembling a truncated pepper-box, bears a cast-brass Britannia and lion (unfortunately hidden by the card number), representing the Britannia Works, Gainsborough. The geared-down tender-mounted boiler pump has covered pinions. Steam washing pipes pass to front and rear rolls via the cock fitting near the steel ladder, the steam supply coming from the cleanly-designed cylinder jacket. A neat capstan-wheel operates the scarifier which is pulled by the rear axle and not the less-strong tender.

F

A Ruston roller bearing the emblem of Ruston & Proctor of Sheaf Ironworks, Lincoln (1899-1918), and the number 43680 which would place the making date at 1910. The roller is registered from 1921 (in the period of Ruston & Hornsby). This is a 10-ton machine with a single cylinder probably 8 in × 12 in of 6 nhp. The front roll fork pivots laterally in a cup bearing. The rolls are in very good, unworn condition. A release valve is fitted to the boiler feed check valve and the pattern of the firebox riveting and stays is evident, together with the spirally-cast steering chain barrel.

An 1897 8-ton SC roller No 2524 made by Wallis & Steevens, Basingstoke, whose many roller designs appeared from 1891 to 1940. The cylinder is 6¼ in × 9 in working at 140 psi. The boiler here is unlagged and reveals the riveted plate construction. The lateral pivoting of the front fork about a central horizontal pin is clearly shown, and the curved seating of the cylinder will be seen to embrace a boiler filling plug. The regulator chest cover carries the usual twin Ramsbottom safety valves; the mechanical lubricator is probably a fitment added since the building date and the ornamental valances on the canopy are of recent date.

Tractors — Overtype and Undertype

This rather limited class of steam vehicle developed from the later designs of steam wagons in many cases, with the important difference that tractors hauled their payloads instead of carrying them. Although the Mann tractor and Garrett 'Agrimotor' have been included in previous sections, these machines also have a claim under the above title. In the mid-1920s, road lorries of the internal-combustion variety began to rival the steam motor tractor (described in Section 3) for medium haulage work.

The overtype and undertype steam tractors were a 'final fling' in this sphere of road transport. At this time, road traffic conditions demanded an ease of general handling and driver comfort which was not afforded by the much slower and more cumbersome traction engine. The steam motor tractor also suffered these faults to a degree and the driver had to stand in order to obtain any reasonable view of the road immediately ahead.

The more obvious advantages of steam tractors were totally enclosed cabins, Ackerman steering, and solid rubber (and later pneumatic) tyres. Important motive features included a short locomotive-type boiler – sometimes with a stayless firebox – working at 230-50 psi, roller bearings and a powerful braking system apart from the engine itself.

E. Foden of Sandbach made the best-known overtype tractor from the mid-1920s to 1930 and varieties are illustrated. It will be noted that the traditional TE element is very much in evidence at the front end. Foden's DCC block had cylinders $4\frac{1}{4}$ in and 7 in × 7 in taking steam at 230 psi maximum pressure. In this and other makers' designs, the countershaft was mounted on the boiler to obtain a closely-built unit, but even so, the driver sat behind a considerable bulk of machinery. Twelve tons could be hauled at the legal maximum of 10 mph. Fodens also made an undertype with a totally enclosed engine and cardan-shaft transmission as opposed to the short chain final drive of the overtypes. A creeper-tracked version was also made, but as far as I know these latter two types have not survived.

Sentinel tractors had a considerable advantage of driver vision from a forward position in front of the water-tube vertical boiler. The engine was undermounted. The Robey overtype was similar in design to the wagon illustrated later, incorporating a stayless boiler with circular firebox, first used by Alley & McLellan in their Sentinel overtype wagon of 1911.

The rugged design of all these tractors is apparent in the examples still existing which perform as well as ever after four decades of use. In fact it was their massive build which gave an average weight of 8 tons, coupled with normal boiler maintenance and steam raising time, that proved the tractors' own enemy in their fight for survival.

An overtype tractor by E. Foden of Sandbach maintained in 'everyday' working condition, made in 1929, No 13358, type D, and weighing 8 tons. The TE-type DCC cylinders are $4\frac{1}{4}$ in and 7 in × 7 in, working at 230 psi from the locomotive boiler. The cylinders and small flywheel are shrouded; the crankshaft and eccentrics have roller bearings. A handwheel, seen near the entrance door, operates one set of two braking systems on the rear axle and wheels. The single chain final drive is just visible; the rear axle sprocket is the outer component of the differential. A winding drum and electric lighting are provided. Ten tons was the 'standard' load hauled.

This is a type C Foden which, like the preceding example, has Ackerman steering, the massive parts of which are detailed together with the transverse leaf spring. Maker's number is 13196 and date 1928. The steering wheel and driving position with the fly-wheel immediately in front provides only fair road visibility. Twin safety valves are enclosed with a brass shroud passing through the canopy, and the four wheels are of all-cast design on solid rubbers. Performance was similar to the D type.

Foden tractor No 13484 named *Talisman*, made in 1930 for agricultural use. Rated at 4½ nhp, the DCC cylinders and motion follow normal Foden practice but a larger fly-wheel is fitted. The lighting system here appears to be electric with oil lamps adapted for electric light. The steering is the TE variety with a solid, pivoting axle connected by short chains to the worm-driven windlass. The small firebox with the attached pump has the ashpan damper on the nearside. The arms of King George V appear on the body signifying Foden's sales to royal estates at that time.

Offside view of Foden D No 13120, made in 1930, showing Ackerman steering quadrant link, the geared-down vertical boiler feed pump mounted on the firebox, chain tensioning arm and support for rear axle adjustment, and the twin brake rings mounted behind the rear wheels. The winding drum behind the nearside rear wheel allows the cable to lead fore or aft and the wheel centre is double-pinned to the axle centre with four available pin holes. Coal rails behind the cab extend the capacity of the bunker which has an access in the cab. A strong channel tow beam is bolted beneath the girder chassis members.

This 'Super' Sentinel No 7527, 1928, is a design preceding the previous tractor, with the same position of the vertical boiler which, in this case, has short water tubes arranged spirally round the central firebox. The undermounted engine, rated 70 bhp approximately, is of duplex cylinder design with inlet and exhaust valves operated by pushrods and camshafts within the crankshaft casing. Final drive is by twin chains forward to the rear axle. The Ackerman steering components are visible. Note the excellent forward driving position, unimpaired by overtype obstructions. The weight is $5\frac{1}{2}$ tons.

A Sentinel timber-hauling and winching tractor No 8756, made in 1933, named *Brutus*. A pair of totally enclosed 100-bhp (maximum) engines are fitted, one undermounted beneath the girder chassis and driving the rear axle by single chain. The second engine is seen overmounted at the rear and drives the small winch drum by enclosed spur reduction gears. The duplex cylinders have separate inlet and exhaust valves operated by the revolving shaft shown which derives its motion from the enclosed crankshaft gearbox. The vertical boiler has crossed water tubes in a detachable firebox and a central top firing chute.

Wagons — Overtype and Undertype

In 1870 J. Yule of Glasgow made a steam wagon with cylinders under its wooden frame. Brown & May constructed one in 1875, both examples having front vertical boilers. In 1896 Thorneycroft produced a 1-ton van also with a vertical boiler which steamed vertical tandem compound cylinders. This example may be taken as the forerunner of commercial steam wagons because development in the intervening years was halted by the ridiculous 'red flag' Act of 1865.

In 1876 the flag was dropped but not the preceding pedestrian. The slower TE and RL developed and fulfilled all haulage tasks until about 1900 when the more familiar names of Mann and Foden appeared as designers and makers of overtype wagons. The 3-ton tare limit for vehicles permitted to exceed 5 mph was most unhelpful to wagon designers of this period.

From 1905 a gradual change from vertical to short locomotive boilers took place. Apart from the Sentinel vertical water tube boiler introduced in 1906, the majority of verticals suffered from inadequate steaming and therefore the greater number of wagons thereafter were overtypes with TE-type motion-work mounted on top of their locomotive boilers; even Sentinel made an overtype wagon in 1911.

Up to 1939 some thirty-five firms made overtype and undertype wagons at various periods using a wide range of fine engines. By the early 1920s the principal makers had been reduced to about fourteen, of whom Sentinels led with undertypes and Foden, Clayton, Garrett, Robey, Wallis & Steevens, Foster, and Burrell were prominent in overtypes. Yorkshire made a combination of both types.

The final undertype wagons of Garrett (1931), Sentinel (1939 home, 1955 overseas), and Foden (1931), included advanced rigid six-wheelers with totally enclosed high-speed engines and pneumatic tyres throughout.

The majority of the later overtypes which exist in fair numbers are of 5 or 6-ton capacity, usually with two speeds, a differential on the 'live' rear axle and a long chain final drive. The 'Super Sentinels' introduced in 1923 had enclosed duplex cylinders $6\frac{3}{4}$ in × 9 in with camshaft valve gear and developed 70 bhp when taking steam at the maximum of 230 psi. A DG series (double-geared drive) came in the late 1920s and included the DG 8 on eight wheels including four front steering. The payload was 15 tons and length 29 ft. Final Sentinels were designated S4-6-8 with cardan-shaft drive and four-cylinder camshaft valve engines developing a maximum of 124 bhp at 255 psi steam pressure. The 'S6' six-wheeler totalled $23\frac{1}{2}$ tons with its 13-ton payload.

Foden's final efforts before turning to diesel in 1931-2 were the 'Speed 6' and '12' with stayless water tube boilers of unique design working at 275 psi. The engine had duplex cylinders 5 in × 7 in with poppet valve gear. A fine example is illustrated. These superb wagons could achieve 60 mph (legal restriction 20 mph) and climb a gradient of 1-in-$3\frac{1}{2}$ with a full load.

The final steam wagons were excellent by any standard, with an elevated, clean exhaust, brilliant acceleration and almost noiseless operation. Given a further forty years of development, the steam wagon might well have proved to be the finest commercial vehicle on the road today.

A Foden overtype wagon No 11538 of 1926, weighing 6 tons and rated at 4 nhp, with cylinders $4\frac{1}{4}$ in and 7 in × 7 in, working at 220 psi on the short locomotive-type boiler. The payload was 6 tons. The authentic Foden pneumatic-tyred wheels may have been fitted after the wagon was new. The long single chain drive – weighing 10 lb per ft – is partially seen on the offside driving to the rear axle differential centre. A water tank is fitted at the rear and Ackerman steering is shown. The large area taken up by the motive element and cab is evident.

Foden overtype wagon of similar specification to the preceding example. No 13708 was made in 1930 and fitted with a 6-ton body. The solid rubber-tyred wheels are original. The single chain is on the nearside and the girder chassis bracing strut and tie-rod are seen below the cab door. Note the massive transverse spring above the front axle, the displacement and mechanical lubricators near the cylinder block, and the rear brake handwheel in the cab. The wagon was restored in 1962 from its second use as a tar tanker-sprayer.

A Sentinel 'Light Super', 6 tons capacity, No 1465. Probably only five were made from spares of earlier 'Supers' for works use 1939-45. The modified design uses duplex cylinders 7 in × 10 in, with camshaft valves working at 250 psi and developing 125 bhp from the class 'S' boiler with double superheater coils. The direct, gearless drive uses a countershaft differential and final twin chains. Pneumatics were fitted when built. The registration date, 31 January 1921, denotes the original chassis date, not the making of the complete wagon. The present owners have fitted the platform body since 1957.

This works photograph shows Foden's last type of steam wagon, the 'Speed 12' of 1930-31, with a payload capacity of 12 tons and officially credited with a maximum speed of 60 mph. The transversely undermounted twin poppet valve engine is partly seen behind the front wheel. A cardan shaft transmits the drive to the twin rear axles, both of which are driven by worm reduction gears. Two speeds are built in the engine, the motion of which revolves on roller and ball bearings. The circular water tube boiler, working at 275 psi, is shaped like a 'drainpipe' elbow of approximately 100°.
(*Photograph by courtesy of Foden Ltd*)

Super Sentinel SG6 type undertype wagon No 8381 made at Shrewsbury in 1930. The vertical boiler in the extreme forward position is the Sentinel DG type in this particular wagon. The lagged steam pipe to the duplex cylinders, $6\frac{3}{4}$ in × 9 in, is seen and also the single chain drive to the rear axle. Approximately 70 bhp was the maximum for brief bursts. Steam and exhaust valves are operated by separate camshafts and pushrods. This wagon is single-geared and always in gear, hence when the engine starts the vehicle moves; an impossible feat with internal combustion. The payload is 6 tons.

Thorneycroft undertype wagon No 39, made in 1900 at Basingstoke and almost certainly unique today. The brewer's special body is a recent restoration. A compound engine with cylinders $4\frac{1}{2}$ in and 7 in × 7 in is mounted midway along the chassis and drives the rear axle via external two-speed pinions and a final reduction gear of double helical gearwheels. The differential is within the large axle gearwheel. The vertical boiler worked at 225 psi being fitted with a triple ring of vertical water tubes and top firing. Note the iron-shod front wheels, Ackerman steering quadrant rack and part of the final gear drive.

The Sentinel undertype wagon in its best and last design, the S4 made in 1934, No 9075. The present owners have rebuilt the vehicle starting from chassis, boiler and wheels only, resulting in a perfect example of its class. A four-cylinder $5\frac{1}{2}$ in × 6 in poppet valve engine develops a maximum of 120 bhp using superheated steam at 255 psi from the front vertical boiler with cross water tubes in a pressed form firebox. Cardan shaft drive has rear axle gearing of spiral bevels and double helical reduction gears. A two-speed gearbox forms an integral part of the engine. Note the entirely 'modern' design of the whole vehicle.

Robeys of Globe Works, Lincoln, made this 6-ton capacity two-speed overtype wagon in 1921. It is probably the only surviving example. The DCC cylinders of $4\frac{1}{4}$ in and $7\frac{1}{4}$ in × 9 in have outside piston valves and work at 250 psi. The stayless 90° 'pistol' or 'drain-pipe' boiler has a circular firebox through which the geared countershaft passes; the outer bearing is seen on the girder chassis. The final long chain drives the rear axle via the usual differential. The picture also shows part of the firebox and the water tank behind it, the suction lift water pipe and cleanly designed cast-steel wheels.

A Sentinel wagon No 8992 made in 1933 of the same S4 class and engine detail as the preceding example. The special water tank body was added in rebuilding in 1958 for supplying rally engines. The steam water pump seen on the chassis is adapted from a 1903 'locomobile' steam car. Below the pump, the standard Sentinel fitting of an engine-driven air compressor for tyre pumping is seen – one of the refinements of the original design. The forward driving position equals any design today. The firm's 'Sentinel' armoured knight decorates the windscreen centre.

Portable Engines

The portable steam engine's history dates from Richard Trevithick's 'high pressure' boiler and engine c 1803. In the early nineteenth century the need arose for shortening and improving the manual tasks in agriculture – particularly threshing. Richard Garrett dated their first portable engine 1824, but no proof of this appears to exist. N. Gough of Salford produced a portable in 1830 and in 1839 W. Howden of Boston constructed a crank-overhead engine mounted on a wheeled oak chassis bearing a horizontal boiler. From 1840-50 Ransomes & May, and Turner (both of Ipswich), Tuxford of Boston, Clayton of Lincoln, and Hornsby of Grantham had all made portables with double-acting single cylinders. Tuxford's design comprised a boiler-mounted oscillating cylinder directly geared to a threshing machine attached to the main wooden bearers.

Portables appeared at the Great Exhibition of 1851. The Hornsby machine with enclosed cylinder over the firebox was judged the best, and the Tuxford, which had vertical cylinders enclosed near the smokebox, burned 4 cwt of coal 'in a day'.

General designs of portable engines changed little over the years and in the eastern counties portable engines were concentrated in some sixty makers, several of whom, including Tuxford, are represented in the illustrations.

Engine efficiency increased and the RAS records that coal consumption for portables fell from 10.79 lb per horsepower per hour to 2.79 lb in the years from 1849 to 1872. R. Garrett achieved a notable advance in portables by the introduction of the DCC cylinder block in an engine shown at Carlisle in 1880. The cylinders were $7\frac{3}{4}$ in and $11\frac{1}{2}$ in × 10 in.

Henceforth the increasing weight of portables became a sore trial for the draught-horse teams by which the engines were moved.

Apart from threshing work, portables drove corn-mills, centrifugal pumps, stone-crushers, dynamos, chaff-cutters and hay-balers, or could work inclined in quarries. By 1910-20, portables achieved finality of design apart from detail improvements such as crosshead trunk-guides and mechanical lubrication. The range made by Ransomes Sims & Jefferies in this period typifies the principal manufacturers' products. Eight sizes in each type of SC, duplex and DCC, were available, ranging from $6\frac{1}{4}$ in × 10 in SC to 11 in and $17\frac{1}{2}$ in × 18 in DCC of 160 bhp with a 6 ft 1 in × 15 in flywheel. On the larger engines the choice of governor gear was either automatic expansion with double slide valves to the high-pressure cylinder or variable expansion eccentric on the high-pressure side with a high-speed governor. Nearly all these engines were available with mechanical straw stokers and larger fireboxes for overseas use. An example of a large DCC Ransomes is illustrated.

Several makers continued with portables into the 1950s and, as mentioned in the Introduction, it is pleasing to record that Robey & Co Ltd of Lincoln* are still making portables for export; probably the one remaining firm in the UK to do so. The unglamorous portable steam engine is therefore commercially viable after 120 years of reliable and beneficent service.

*Since this was written, it has been reported (January 1969) that the firm is selling out.

Charles Burrell's SCC 10-nhp portable engine No 2363, made in 1901; the sole survivor of the six of the type made 1891-1908. The massive cylinder block is probably 7 in and 11 in bore. The stroke is 12 in. The regulator-lever linkage is seen, also a Salter safety valve, Pickering governor, displacement lubricator and chimney support – all mounted on the regulator chest. Twin flywheels assist steady running and provide a variable speed for belt drives. The protected water-gauge is a modern pattern with asbestos ring cock packings. Note the boiler lagging over the firebox and a repair strip on the back plate.

A 4-nhp portable by Clayton & Shuttleworth, Lincoln. This late SC type is fitted with oil ring crankshaft bearings; the fillers for the internal reservoirs are seen at the base of the castings which are mounted on a flat plate seating. A tie-bar connects the crankshaft assembly to the cylinder block. The crank head has a split marine-type bearing. Cylinder fittings include a Salter safety valve, steam delivery to the injector, Pickering governor and mechanical lubricator. The feed pump has a separate boiler delivery valve. There is a steam supply take-off from the exhaust for feed water warming, and a blower entering the chimney base.

This large SC 8-nhp portable by W. Foster, Lincoln, is one of their final portables and made in 1942, No 14737. Made for Lincolnshire farm work, the wheels are unusually wide and of double channel, rolled and welded T-ring construction to which the tyres are riveted. The regulator is operated by the unequal lever. A cross-arm governor (not belted up here) works a simple part-rotating barrel throttle in the cylinder block. The crankshaft bearings have cast flat webs bolted to triangular steel plate boiler supports. Here, it will be noted, the crank-head bearing is the gib and cotter design.

Compound portable No 39 of 6 nhp, made by Farmers' Foundry Co, Great Ryburgh, Norfolk, in 1922. This is one of the three existing examples. Apart from the rarity of DCC portables today, the engine possesses the unusual features of cranks at 180° instead of the normal 90° and a horizontal Pickering governor, directly belt-driven from the crankshaft. The regulator arm works left and right and the mechanical lubricator is driven by the high-pressure valve rod; the linkage is seen below the trunk guides. The main bearings are split at 45° so that the thrust line is not at 90° to the securing studs.

A portable made in 1921 by Ruston & Hornsby, Lincoln. A SC engine rated 4 nhp. The chimney is in the usual travelling position when horse-draught was used. Having no wheel brakes, portables were 'braked' on inclines by allowing a rear wheel to ride on the 'skidpan', shown here attached to the front axle bracket. The maker's ratchet-driven mechanical lubricator and linkage is of interest, also the lagging cover over the valve chest and the inspection plate in the outer firebox shell. The rear wheels are mounted on stub axles attached to boiler pad plates. A large organ whistle is probably a recent addition.

Two-nhp engine by William Tuxford, Boston, Lincs, a pioneer of portable engines. No 138 was made in 1880, and is one of the two working Tuxfords remaining from the production years 1826-87. The delicate motion work, heavy Watt governor, graceful cast crankshaft support brackets and large flywheel are typical of mid-nineteenth century engine construction. The crank-head bearing is the split type and the direct eccentric-driven boiler feed pump is mounted on the smokebox offside. The discharge is seen on the extreme left. A small Salter safety valve is head-high to the owner-driver. There is no mechanical lubricator, but a globe oil feeder on the valve chest.

Ransomes Sims & Jefferies SC 5-nhp made in 1908, with $7\frac{3}{4}$ in × 12 in cylinder. Here the cylinder-to-bearing stay is solid. The Salter safety valve is attached to the regulator valve casting (below the Pickering governor pulley). The boiler back plate carries a pair of water level test cocks as standby in case of water-gauge failure. An unloaded threshing drum is being driven with only 20 psi showing on the gauge. One hundred and twenty psi was normal working pressure, giving a sustained bhp of 18. There are four parallel crosshead guide-bars, vertically driven feed pump, exhaust feed water takeoff and a small whistle near the cylinder rear cover.

Eight-nhp SC Ruston & Proctor No 29011, driving a Ransomes medium-type threshing machine No 52129, size 54 in, and a straw-baler. The pressure gauge registers about 40 psi and the cylinder is 10 in × 12 in stroke. Twin Salter safety valves are fitted, centrally-acting governor, and fore-and-aft regulator control. On the offside, Ruston's patent steam-jacketed stay connects the crankshaft bearing pedestal to the cylinder block – a device to minimise expansion problems. The cylinder and crankshaft bearings are mounted on flat machined seatings. A spark-arrester appears on the chimney top. This threshing set-up was common up to the 1880s.

Six-nhp engine by Ransomes No 36030, 1925, showing the nearside and including an observer having contemporary memories. The curved spoke flywheel (also seen on some early stationary engines) was at one time thought to lessen the cooling stress in flywheel castings. The long guide casting for the valve spindle is attached to the valve chest only, the cover of which carries the well-known oval brass maker's numberplate. A strong reinforcing boiler plate supports the manhole cover and dogs. The firebox rivet and stay pattern is clearly detailed. A normal bhp of 22 would be achieved on a working pressure of 120 psi.

My copy photograph shows a large Ransomes compound engine rated at 90 bhp complete with all accessories, when new in the early 1920s. An automatic expansion valve in the high-pressure steam chest is operated by the roller chain driven governor. The twin flywheels are 6 ft × 10 in face, cylinders 9 in and 14 in × 16 in working at 150 psi. An exhaust feed water heater lies along the boiler, the regulator control is conveniently low on the nearside. A large straw-burning firebox and chimney spark-arrester denotes an export engine, the large size of which is shown by the access ladders and handrails.
(*Original by courtesy of Ransomes Sims & Jefferies Ltd*)

I include a third view of a Ransomes (this is No 14704 of 1903, 6 nhp) to give a reasonable total general arrangement for possible model work. Little change is evident during the span of years. The governor is a modified Watt-type with a lower lifting collar into which the throttle valve yoke fits. The cotter adjusted crank bearing is well shown and the crank webs are unmachined round section as forged. Other typical Ransomes' features are square flanged chimney base, domed hub-caps, waisted circular front axle support and raised section of the upper pair of straight guide-bars. A pair of displacement lubricators is fitted to the cylinder.

Six-nhp portable by Marshall Sons & Co, Gainsborough, made about 1910. The generally plain robust design of portables explains their commercial longevity. Marshalls' wheel spokes are made of adjacent bent strip triangles, forming strong edgeways spoking. A cross-arm governor is partly seen; the rear cylinder cover has a central lubricator, adjacent to which is the Salter safety valve. A massive crank is driven by a wedged and cottered connecting rod bearing. Main bearings have adjusting side set-bolts. The back plate carries a blow down valve at the bottom flanked by washout plugs. A semi-protected water gauge shows the correct 'half-glass' level.

The last engine to bear Charles Burrell's name. *King George V* was made by R. Garrett at Leiston, Suffolk, 11 June 1932, No 4094 (Burrells closed in 1928). It is 8 nhp with a SC 9 in × 12 in working at 160 psi. The working order weight is 11¾ tons. Garrett's covering of the two-speed gears is prominent on the nearside. The pair of whistles sprouting from the regulator chest are additions. In our leave-taking we surmise the near spectator's thoughts in 1956 when this imposing and elegant chimney was photographed.

Acknowledgments

The following engineering firms and individuals have given information and assistance which has been greatly appreciated: Ransomes Sims & Jefferies Ltd, Ipswich; Foden Ltd, Sandbach; Wallis & Steevens Ltd, Basingstoke; Marshall Sons & Co Ltd, Gainsborough; Robey & Co Ltd, Lincoln; Fearnleys, Engineers, Castleford; L. J. Orvis, Esq, Works Historian, Ransomes Sims & Jefferies Ltd; The Reverend R. C. Stebbing; Major H. D. Marshall; T. B. Paisley, Esq; F. R. Howling, Esq; J. Crawley, Esq; A. Bloom, Esq; R. H. Temple, Esq; also numerous engine owners and drivers.

Bibliography

Aveling-Barford Ltd	*100 Years of Road Rollers*
Bonnett, H.	*The Saga of the Steam Plough*
Clark, R. H.	*Chronicles of a Country Works* (History of Burrells) *The Development of the English Traction Engine* *The Development of the Steam Wagon* *A Short History of Savages Ltd* *Steam Engine Builders of Lincolnshire* *Steam Engine Builders of Norfolk* *Steam Engine Builders of Suffolk, Essex and Cambridgeshire* 'Traction Engines Not So Well Known', *Model Engineer* (1949)
Crawley, J.	'Steaming', *Journal of the National Traction Engine Club*
Hughes, W. J.	*Traction Engines Worth Modelling* *A Century of Traction Engines*
Kidner, R. H.	*The Steam Lorry Album*
Spence, C. C.	*God Speed the Plow*
True, J. B., and Kinsey, B. K.	*The Traction Engine Register*
Whitehead, R. A.	*Garretts of Leiston*
Wright, P.	*Traction Engines*

Also steam engine manufacturers' catalogues and literature, now collectors' items.

Index to Plates

General Index